Mysterious Maths

Alison Head

In a cave far away, lives a powerful wizard named Whimstaff. He spends his days finding the answers to ancient Maths problems and has parchments filled with notorious numbers. In this book, Whimstaff shares his knowledge to help you to master the art of Mathematics.

Whimstaff has a goblin assistant named Pointy, who is very clever. Pointy helps Whimstaff perfect his spells and gets annoyed with the laziness of Mugly and Bugly,

his fat pet frogs. They spend most of their time eating and sleeping and do as little work as possible.

Pointy also helps Whimstaff look after Miss Snufflebeam, a young dragon, who is rather clumsy and often loses Whimstaff's numbers!

Wizard Whimstaff and his friends are very happy solving Maths problems. Join them on a magical quest to win the Trophy of Maths Wizardry!

Contents

Super Symbols

Welcome, young apprentice.
I'm Wizard Whimstaff and I'm going to help you become a maths wizard. Now listen carefully.
Maths symbols give you information or instructions about the numbers before or after them in a problem. Look at these:

< means less than.
3 is less than 4, so 3 < 4.

> means more than.
6 is more than 5, so 6 > 5.

= means equal to, or equals.
3 + 4 = 7.

Task 1 Look at the jars of flies and decide which symbol (<, >, =) describes the relationship between them. Just do your best.

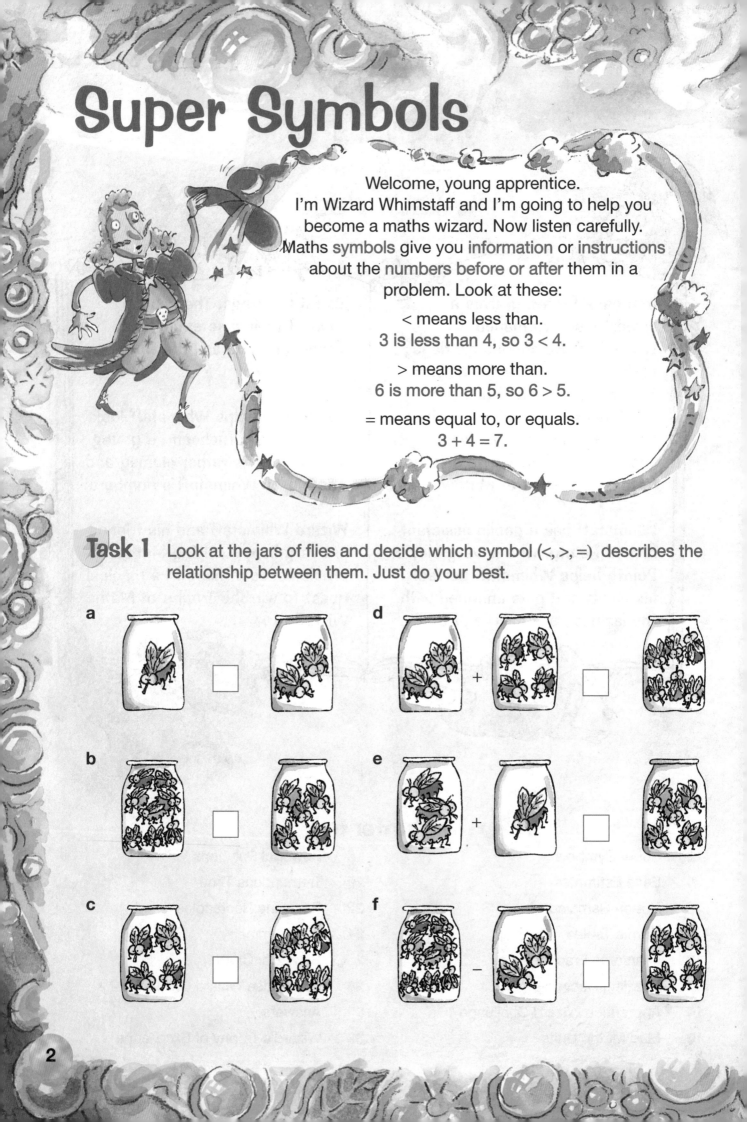

a

b

c

d +

e +

f −

Task 2 Excellent work! Now try these. Just choose one number from the cauldron to complete each problem.

a
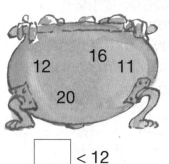

12 16 11
20

☐ < 12

b
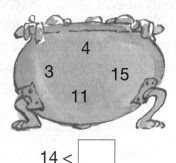

4
3 15
11

14 < ☐

c
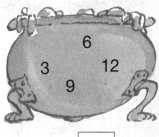

6
3 12
9

3 = 9 − ☐

d
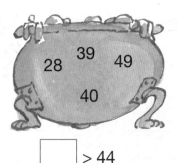

39
28 49
40

☐ > 44

e
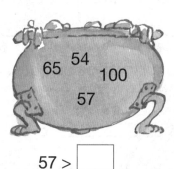

54
65 100
57

57 > ☐

f
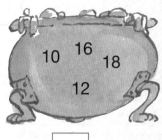

16
10 18
12

65 + ☐ = 77

Task 3 Hey Presto! Can you write true or false next to these?

a 3 + 3 + 3 = 9 _____

b 14 + 2 > 18 _____

c 12 − 3 > 8 _____

d 22 + 3 < 26 _____

e 35 − 17 < 17 _____

f 18 + 17 = 37 _____

Sorcerer's Skill Check

You're doing well. Now let's see what you've learnt about maths symbols. Can you fill in the gaps in these?

a 13 − 4 ☐ 8

b 20 + 2 ☐ 22

c 14 + 3 ☐ 12

d 111 + 1 ☐ 112

e 125 − 15 ☐ 112

f 121 − 8 ☐ 114

Super! Now collect your first silver shield to put on the trophy at the back of the book!

Eerie Estimates

Hello! I'm Pointy, Wizard Whimstaff's assistant. **Estimating** is a brilliant way to check your answers when you're tackling maths problems and it's easy when you know how! Just round each number up or down to the nearest multiple of ten or a hundred to make them easier to add up or subtract quickly.

Here's some examples:
6 is closer to 10 than 0, so we round it up to 10.
43 is closer to 0 than 100, so we round it down to 0.

Task 1 Let's start by rounding these numbers up or down to the nearest multiple of ten.

a 23 _____   b 48 _____   c 91 _____   d 114 _____

Now round these up or down to the nearest multiple of 100.

e 120 _____   f 180 _____   g 240 _____   h 390 _____

Task 2 Now look at the number lines and estimate what number is hidden behind each star. You'll soon get the hang of it!

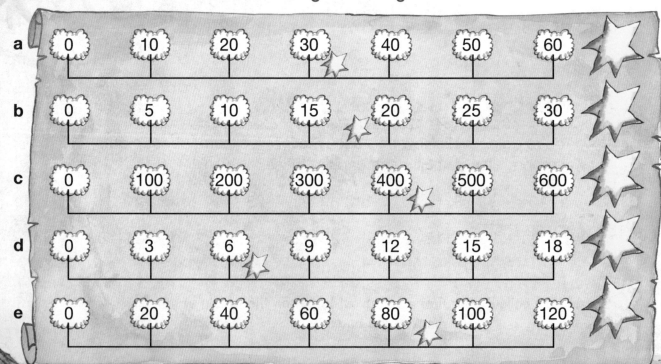

Task 3 Super! Now use estimation to help you pick the right answer to these problems. Circle the answer you think is correct.

a 62 + 49 =   96   111   49   210

d 59 + 29 =   112   108   120   88

b 141 + 122 =   220   290   283   263

e 201 + 111 =   214   312   410   420

c 19 + 158 =   177   207   217   157

f 97 + 131 =   318   207   228   197

Task 4 Look at the magic potion bottles and estimate how much potion is left in each. Circle your answer. Practice makes perfect!

a

$\frac{1}{2}$ $\frac{2}{3}$ $\frac{3}{4}$

b

$\frac{1}{3}$ $\frac{1}{2}$ $\frac{2}{3}$

c

$\frac{1}{4}$ $\frac{1}{2}$ $\frac{3}{3}$

d

$\frac{1}{3}$ $\frac{2}{3}$ $\frac{3}{4}$

Sorcerer's Skill Check

Use estimation to help you pick numbers from the cauldron to fill the gaps in the sums below!

16
35   19
120
26

a 14 + 21 = ☐

b 27 + ☐ = 43

c ☐ + 81 = 100

d ☐ + 36 = 156

e 124 + ☐ = 150

My head hurts! But you're set to collect a shield now for your trophy.
Well done!

Rotten Remainders

Brain cell alert! It's Mugly and Bugly again. Sometimes you can't divide one number exactly into another and you get left with some spare.

5 pies divided between 2 of us means 2 pies each plus one to fight over.

Wizard Whimstaff says the leftover number is called the remainder, but we call it lunch!

Task 1 We've invited all our froggy friends round for tea. Can you divide the flies fairly between them? Circle how many flies each frog will get, then write the remainder in the box.

a ☐   **b** ☐   **c** ☐

d ☐   **e** ☐   **f** ☐

Task 2 Well, aren't you clever! All those yummy flies left over for us. While we tuck in, try working out the remainders in these problems.

a $13 \div 2 =$ ☐ 6 ☐ remainder ☐ I ☐

b $10 \div 3 =$ ☐ remainder ☐

c $7 \div 3 =$ ☐ remainder ☐

d $8 \div 5 =$ ☐ remainder ☐

e $22 \div 4 =$ ☐ remainder ☐

f $33 \div 5 =$ ☐ remainder ☐

g $28 \div 3 =$ ☐ remainder ☐

h $27 \div 5 =$ ☐ remainder ☐

i $46 \div 4 =$ ☐ remainder ☐

j $25 \div 2 =$ ☐ remainder ☐

Task 3

Croak! If you're dividing up some units, like pounds or metres, you can write the remainders in smaller units, like pence or cm. Just break the number into the smaller units first. Try these while we take a nap!

a £5 ÷ 4 = [500] p ÷ 4 = [125] p, or £ [1.25] p

b £6 ÷ 5 = [   ] p ÷ 5 = [   ] p, or £ [   ] p

c £3 ÷ 2 = [   ] p ÷ 2 = [   ] p, or £ [   ] p

d 5m ÷ 2 = [   ] cm ÷ 2 = [   ] cm, or [   ] m

e 9m ÷ 4 = [   ] cm ÷ 4 = [   ] cm, or [   ] m

f 18m ÷ 8 = [   ] cm ÷ 8 = [   ] cm, or [   ] m

Task 4

Wizard Whimstaff buys Wizzo's Wonderful Webs for his spiders. If the new webs come in boxes of 3, how many boxes does he need for each group of spiders? Work out the problems, then round up the remainder. We've done the first one to help you. Croak!

a 29 spiders need [10] boxes

b 38 spiders need [   ] boxes

c 61 spiders need [   ] boxes

d 71 spiders need [   ] boxes

e 83 spiders need [   ] boxes

29 spiders ÷ 3 = 9 boxes plus 2 spiders without webs, so Wizard Whimstaff needs 10 boxes in all.

Sorcerer's Skill Check

Grub's up! We're off for lunch while you tackle these. Work out the answers to each pair of problems, then colour in the largest answer.

a 17 ÷ 3 = _____ r_____

b 12 ÷ 10 = _____ r_____

c 19 ÷ 4 = _____ r_____

  29 ÷ 5 = _____ r_____

  8 ÷ 5 = _____ r_____

  14 ÷ 3 = _____ r_____

You're going to make a super Maths Wizard! Take another shield!

Terrific Tables

Slurp!
We're Mugly and Bugly,
the lazy frogs. Maths is too much
like hard work for us, but you can make
things easier. Learning your times
tables helps you to work out
problems more quickly. While we have a
snack, practise your 2, 3, 4, 5 and 10
times tables with these exercises.

Task 1 Brain cell alert! Can you fill in the missing numbers on these lily pads?

a 2 | 4 | ☐ | ☐ | 10 | 12 | 14 | 16 | ☐

b 3 | ☐ | 9 | 12 | ☐ | 18 | 21 | ☐

c 4 | ☐ | ☐ | 16 | 20 | 24 | 28 | ☐

d 10 | 15 | ☐ | 25 | 30 | ☐ | 40 | ☐

e 10 | 20 | 30 | ☐ | ☐ | 60 | 70 | 80 | ☐

Task 2 Croak! Multiplying numbers saves you having to add them all up. Can you write the missing numbers in the multiplication problems?

a $3 + 3 + 3 + 3 = 12$ → $\boxed{4} \times 3 = 12$

b $2 + 2 + 2 + 2 + 2 + 2 + 2 = 14$ → $\boxed{} \times 2 = 14$

c $3 + 3 + 3 + 3 + 3 + 3 + 3 + 3 + 3 + 3 + 3 + 3 = 36$ → $\boxed{} \times 3 = 36$

d $2 + 2 + 2 + 2 + 2 + 2 + 2 + 2 + 2 + 2 = 20$ → $\boxed{} \times 2 = 20$

e $4 + 4 + 4 + 4 + 4 + 4 + 4 = 28$ → $\boxed{} \times 4 = 28$

8

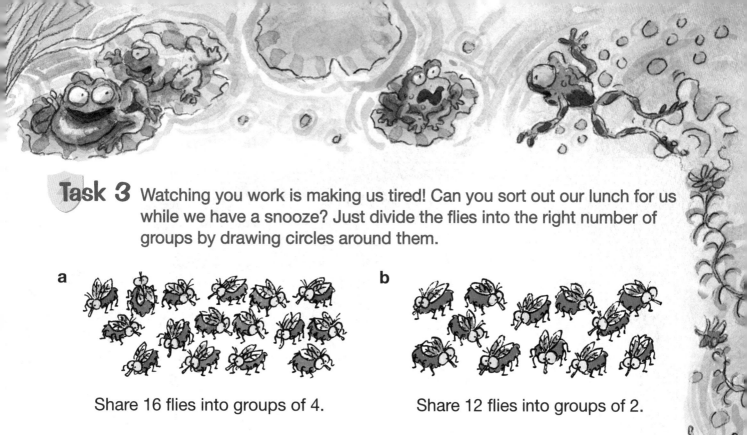

Task 3 Watching you work is making us tired! Can you sort out our lunch for us while we have a snooze? Just divide the flies into the right number of groups by drawing circles around them.

a

Share 16 flies into groups of 4.

b

Share 12 flies into groups of 2.

c

Share 9 flies into groups of 3.

d

Share 15 flies into groups of 5.

e

Share 20 flies into groups of 10.

Sorcerer's Skill Check

This must be a job for Pointy! Use what you've learnt about tables to match up the pairs of problems which have the same answer.

a 3×4	**b** 2×3	**c** 4×4	**d** 2×10	**e** 5×3	**f** 2×2
4×1	3×5	8×2	3×2	5×4	6×2

Excellent work, my apprentice. Add another silver shield to your trophy!

Fearsome Fractions

Fractions allow you to divide whole numbers up into smaller parts. Just remember that the bottom half of the fraction, called the denominator, tells you how many parts the whole number is divided into. The top half, called the numerator, tells you how many parts are in the fraction.

So with $\frac{3}{4}$, the whole number is divided into four parts, and the fraction represents three of them.

If the denominator and the numerator are the same, the fraction represents 1.

You'll soon get the hang of it!

Task 1 Super! Look at these fractions, then colour in the section of the spiders' webs to represent them. The denominator tells you how many sections the web needs to be split into and the numerator tells you how many to colour in.

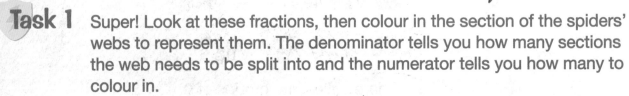

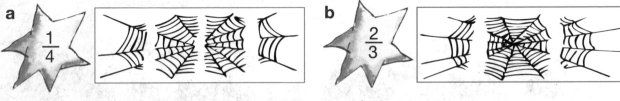

Task 2 These are harder! Look at the potion bottles and write down the fraction that represents how much potion is left.

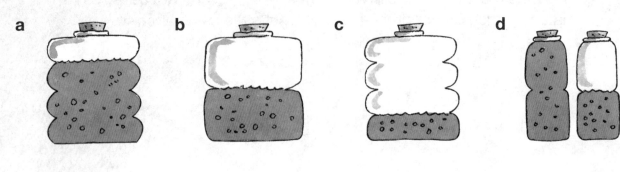

Task 3 Look at these and fill in the gaps.

a $1\frac{1}{2} = \frac{3}{2}$

b $1\frac{1}{3} = \frac{4}{\boxed{}}$

c $2\frac{1}{2} = \frac{5}{\boxed{}}$

d $1\frac{1}{4} = \frac{\boxed{}}{4}$

e $2 = \frac{\boxed{}}{4}$

f $2\frac{1}{4} = \frac{\boxed{}}{4}$

> When the numerator is bigger than the denominator, the fraction is bigger than one and it can be written as a mixed number, with both whole numbers and a fraction.

Task 4 Now try these. Draw lines to link pairs of fractions that add up to **3**.

a $1\frac{1}{2}$ b $\frac{1}{2}$ c $\frac{1}{3}$ d $\frac{3}{4}$ e $2\frac{1}{5}$

$\frac{4}{5}$ $2\frac{2}{3}$ $1\frac{1}{2}$ $2\frac{1}{4}$ $2\frac{1}{2}$

Sorcerer's Skill Check

Practice makes perfect! Just one more exercise to go. Mugly and Bugly are having pizza for lunch and it looks like they've already started! Look at the pizzas and answer the questions.

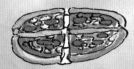  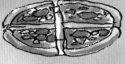 

a How many whole pizzas are there? _____

b How many pizza quarters are left altogether? _____

c How much pizza is left, as a mixed number? _____

d How many pizza quarters are missing? _____

You'll be as clever as Pointy soon! Have another shield for your trophy.

Dazzling Decimals

Now, my apprentice,
it's time to learn about decimals.
Like fractions, decimals are numbers which
fit between whole numbers and break them
into tenths, hundredths and so on.

$$\frac{1}{10} = 0.1 \qquad \frac{1}{100} = 0.01$$

Don't worry if it seems hard at first.
Just do your best.

Task 1 My magic reveals the decimal numbers between whole numbers. Can you fill in the gaps?

a

| 3.1 | 3.2 | ☆ | 3.4 | 3.5 | ☆ | 3.7 | 3.8 | ☆ | 4.0 |

b

| 2.21 | 2.22 | 2.23 | ☆ | 2.25 | 2.26 | ☆ | 2.28 | 2.29 | 2.30 | ☆ |

c

| 10.1 | 10.2 | 10.3 | ☆ | ☆ | 10.6 | ☆ | ☆ | ☆ |

d

| 6.91 | ☆ | ☆ | 6.94 | 6.95 | ☆ | ☆ | 6.98 | 6.99 | ☆ |

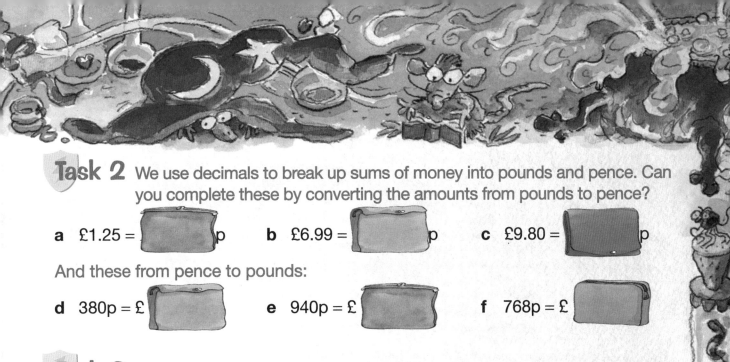

Task 2
We use decimals to break up sums of money into pounds and pence. Can you complete these by converting the amounts from pounds to pence?

a £1.25 = [   ] p   **b** £6.99 = [   ] p   **c** £9.80 = [   ] p

And these from pence to pounds:

d 380p = £ [   ]   **e** 940p = £ [   ]   **f** 768p = £ [   ]

Task 3
We also use decimals to break metres up into centimetres. Can you find the matching pairs?

a 1.25m	**b** 0.5m	**c** 130cm	**d** 2.8m
1.3m	50cm	280cm	125cm

Task 4
Now let's look at how fractions and decimals can represent the same number. Look at the potion bottles and fill in the amount of potion in the equivalent decimal or fraction below.

a   **b**   **c**   **d**   **e**

_____   _____   _____   _____   _____

Sorcerer's Skill Check

Finally, let's check what you've learnt. Put these numbers in order, starting with the smallest.

a 235p	_____	**b** 135cm	_____	**c** 99cm	_____
£2.40	_____	1m	_____	242cm	_____
99p	_____	201cm	_____	$2\frac{1}{2}$ cm	_____
£1.99	_____	895cm	_____	58cm	_____

Slurp! Time to add another silver shield to your trophy!

Apprentice Wizard Challenge 1

Challenge 1 Choose the correct symbol: <, > or = .

a 190 + 120 300 **b** 78 − 6 72 **c** 6 × 4 25

d 8 × 5 38 **e** 18 + 2 + 2 21 **f** 24 − 11 13

Challenge 2 These sums show how many magic beans Wizard Whimstaff needs for his spells. Use your estimating skills to work out which box of beans he should buy for each one.

a 70 + 8 Wizard Whimstaff should buy a box of _____ magic beans.

b 32 + 12 Wizard Whimstaff should buy a box of _____ magic beans.

c 68 + 29 Wizard Whimstaff should buy a box of _____ magic beans.

d 12 + 32 Wizard Whimstaff should buy a box of _____ magic beans.

e 41 + 21 Wizard Whimstaff should buy a box of _____ magic beans.

Challenge 3 Colour in the lily pads which have problems that don't divide exactly.

a 15 ÷ 3 **b** 18 ÷ 4 **c** 14 ÷ 5 **d** 12 ÷ 5 **e** 9 ÷ 3

f 45 ÷ 10 **g** 17 ÷ 3 **h** 9 ÷ 4 **i** 6 ÷ 2 **j** 10 ÷ 3

Challenge 4 Complete the grid.

x	2	3	4	5	10
2		6	8		20
3		9	12		30
4	8		16	20	
5	10	15			50
10	20		40	50	

Challenge 5 Colour in the sections of the webs to represent each of these fractions. Then put them in order by numbering them, starting with the smallest.

a $\frac{2}{3}$ b $\frac{1}{2}$ c $\frac{5}{6}$ d $\frac{1}{3}$ e $\frac{1}{6}$

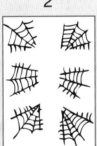 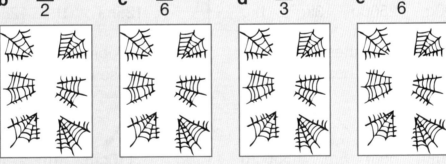 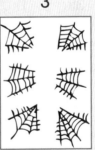 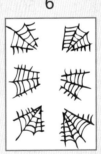

_____   _____   _____   _____   _____

Challenge 6 Convert these decimals to fractions.

a 0.25 _____   b 0.75 _____   c 0.1 _____   d 1.5 _____   e 2.75 _____

Count how many challenges you got right and put stars on the test tube to show your score. Then have another silver shield for your trophy!

6

5

4

3

2

1

Challenge Score

Mad Metric Units

We use standard metric units to measure length, mass and capacity, like this:

Length
1 kilometre (km) = 1000 metres
1 metre (m) = 100 centimetres (cm), 1 cm = 10 millimetres (mm)

Mass
1 kilogram (kg) = 1000 grams (g)

Capacity
1 litre (l) = 1000 millilitres (ml)

It's easy when you know how!
Try these.

Task 1 Can you help me find the best ingredients for Wizard Whimstaff's spells? Draw a circle around your answer.

a Help me find the heaviest flying pig.

250g   2500g   3kg   1kg

b Which cauldron will hold the most?

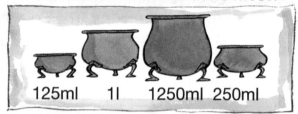

125ml   1l   1250ml   250ml

c Now I need the fittest flea. Which can jump the furthest?

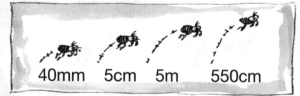

40mm   5cm   5m   550cm

d My broomstick is 112cm long. Which of these is nearly the same length?

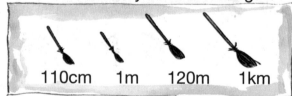

110cm   1m   120m   1km

Task 2 Practice makes perfect! Now can you help me check how much potion is left in these bottles?

a  This bottle holds 500ml. If I use 250ml, how much is left?

b This bottle holds 1 litre. If I use 600ml, how much is left?

c  This one holds 3000ml. If I use 1 litre, how much is left?

Task 3
Super! You're being a great help. Now let's make sure Wizard Whimstaff will have enough magic beans for his spells.

a The jar holds 3000g of magic beans. If Wizard Whimstaff needs 1kg, how much will be left? _____

b Wizard Whimstaff drops 1kg of beans on the floor by mistake, and Mugly and Bugly gobble up 400g. What weight of beans is left? _____

c I need to weigh out beans for two spells. The first needs 1kg of beans and the second needs 250g. What weight of beans do I need altogether? _____

Task 4
Miss Snufflebeam has spilt some growth potion onto Wizard Whimstaff's broomsticks.

a One of the broomsticks was 1m long but it has grown by 32cm.

How long is it now in centimetres?

b Another broomstick used to be 250cm long but it has doubled in length.

How long is it now in metres?

c The longest broomstick is now 6m long! If I saw 200cm off to use as firewood.

How long will it be in centimetres?

Sorcerer's Skill Check

Nearly there! Now let's see what you've learnt about metric units. Just join up the matching pairs.

a 8cm   b 2 litres   c 100cm   d 4000g   e 2000m

4kg   1m   2km   80mm   2000ml

Good work, my apprentice! Stick a silver shield on your trophy.

17

Powerful Polygons

To become a maths whizz you need to learn about **polygons**! They are super shapes with **three or more straight sides** and you can find them all over the place!

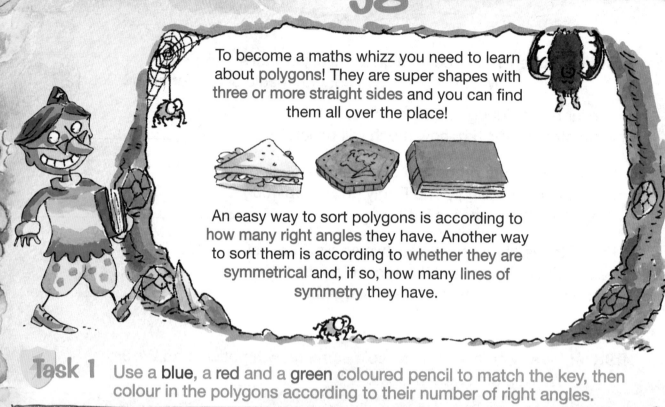

An easy way to sort polygons is according to how many right angles they have. Another way to sort them is according to whether they are symmetrical and, if so, how many lines of symmetry they have.

Task 1 Use a **blue**, a **red** and a **green** coloured pencil to match the key, then colour in the polygons according to their number of right angles.

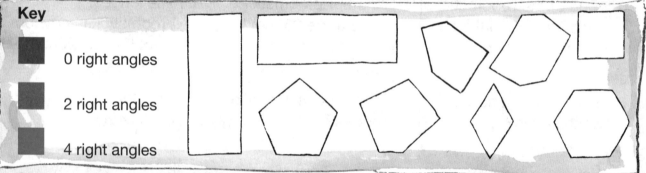

Key

■ 0 right angles

■ 2 right angles

■ 4 right angles

Task 2 Practice makes perfect! Can you complete these shapes so they are regular polygons?

a

b

c

d

e

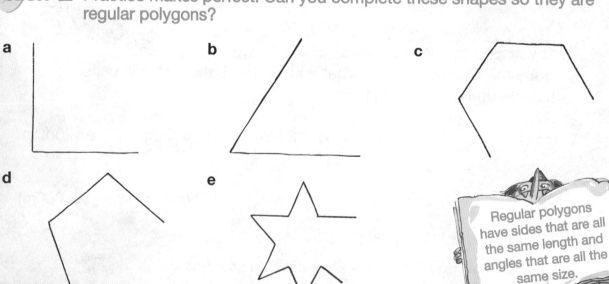

Regular polygons have sides that are all the same length and angles that are all the same size.

Can you draw the lines of symmetry into these polygons, then colour in the ones that have two lines of symmetry? It's easy when you know how!

a   b   c   d

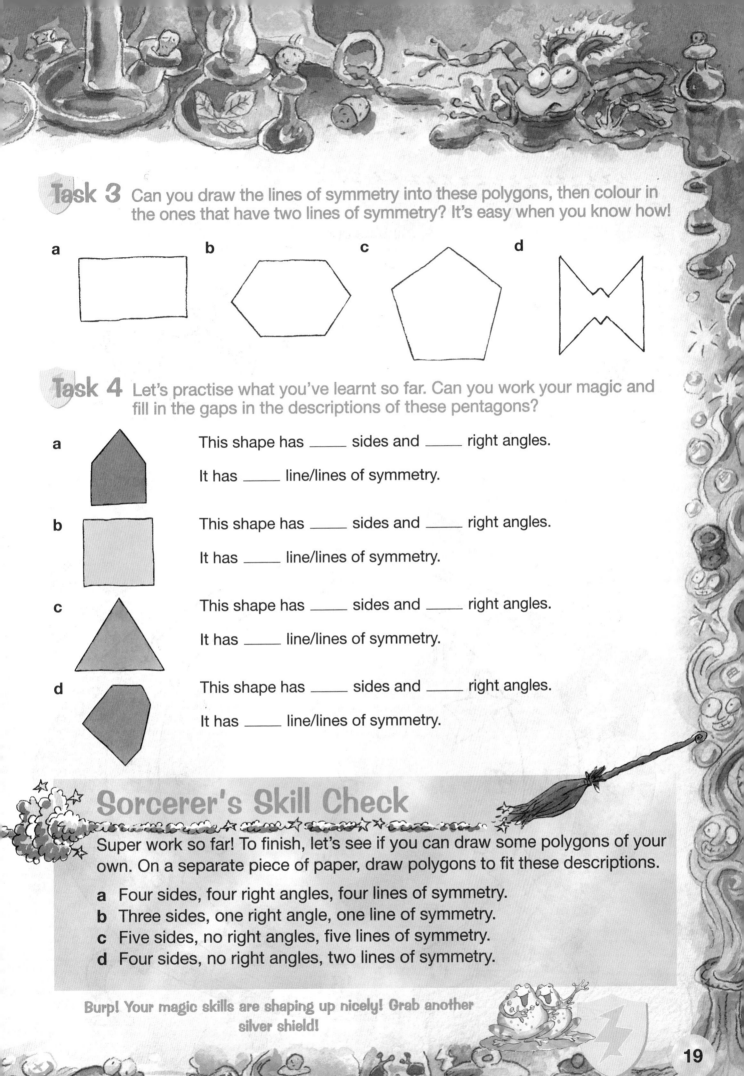

Task 4   Let's practise what you've learnt so far. Can you work your magic and fill in the gaps in the descriptions of these pentagons?

a   This shape has _____ sides and _____ right angles.

It has _____ line/lines of symmetry.

b   This shape has _____ sides and _____ right angles.

It has _____ line/lines of symmetry.

c   This shape has _____ sides and _____ right angles.

It has _____ line/lines of symmetry.

d   This shape has _____ sides and _____ right angles.

It has _____ line/lines of symmetry.

Sorcerer's Skill Check

Super work so far! To finish, let's see if you can draw some polygons of your own. On a separate piece of paper, draw polygons to fit these descriptions.

a   Four sides, four right angles, four lines of symmetry.
b   Three sides, one right angle, one line of symmetry.
c   Five sides, no right angles, five lines of symmetry.
d   Four sides, no right angles, two lines of symmetry.

Burp! Your magic skills are shaping up nicely! Grab another silver shield!

Tremendous Time

Task 1 We use the 24 hour clock to tell us when it's time for our next meal. Can you fill in the gaps while we have a snooze?

20

Task 2

We hate waking up, but Pointy's collection of alarm clocks always disturbs our naps. Can you tell us which alarm is about to ring by drawing a circle around the digital readout that matches the clock face?

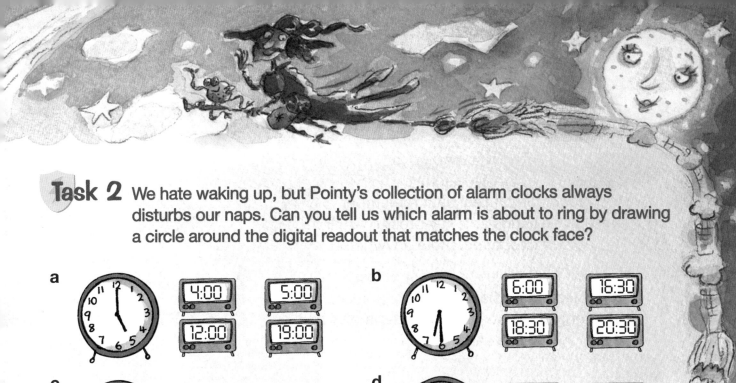

a
4:00 5:00
12:00 19:00

b
6:00 16:30
18:30 20:30

c
9:00 18:45
16:45 20:45

d
12:20 14:30
2:20 22:20

Task 3

Slurp! Here's a list of things Pointy has to do today. Boring! Can you put them in the correct order by numbering them from 1 to 6?

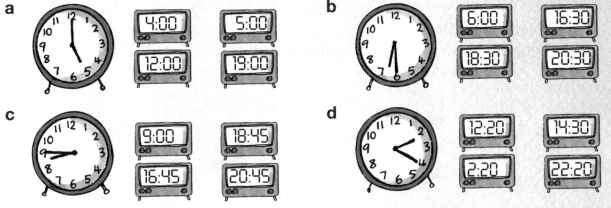

a ◯ 22:30 Feed Mugly and Bugly, again!

b ◯ 7:30 Breakfast with Wizard Whimstaff

c ◯ 12:10 Lunch with Miss Snufflebeam

d ◯ 11:00 Feed Mugly and Bugly

e ◯ 17:45 Collect frogspawn for new spell

f ◯ 9:20 Take the broomstick for a spin

Sorcerer's Skill Check

Grub's up! Draw hands on the clock face to match these digital alarm readouts.

a  7:30

b  11:45

c  24:00

d 22:15

Super! Time for another silver shield!

Revolting Rectangles

I want to teach you about **rectangles**. Just remember these three things and hey presto, you'll be able to spot a rectangle anywhere!

⭐ Rectangles **have four sides**.
⭐ Rectangles **have four right angles**.
⭐ Rectangles' opposite sides are **parallel and the same length**.

Now have a go at these exercises.

Task 1 Abracadabra! Look at the magic shapes below. Answer the questions about each one to help you decide if it's a rectangle. Circle yes or no.

a

Does this shape have four sides?	Yes No
Does it have four right angles?	Yes No
Are its opposite sides of equal length and parallel?	Yes No
Is it a rectangle?	Yes No

b

Does this shape have four sides?	Yes No
Does it have four right angles?	Yes No
Are its opposite sides of equal length and parallel?	Yes No
Is it a rectangle?	Yes No

c

Does this shape have four sides?	Yes No
Does it have four right angles?	Yes No
Are its opposite sides of equal length and parallel?	Yes No
Is it a rectangle?	Yes No

d

Does this shape have four sides?	Yes No
Does it have four right angles?	Yes No
Are its opposite sides of equal length and parallel?	Yes No
Is it a rectangle?	Yes No

Task 2 Use your magic to circle the rectangle in each group of crystals.

a   b   c   d

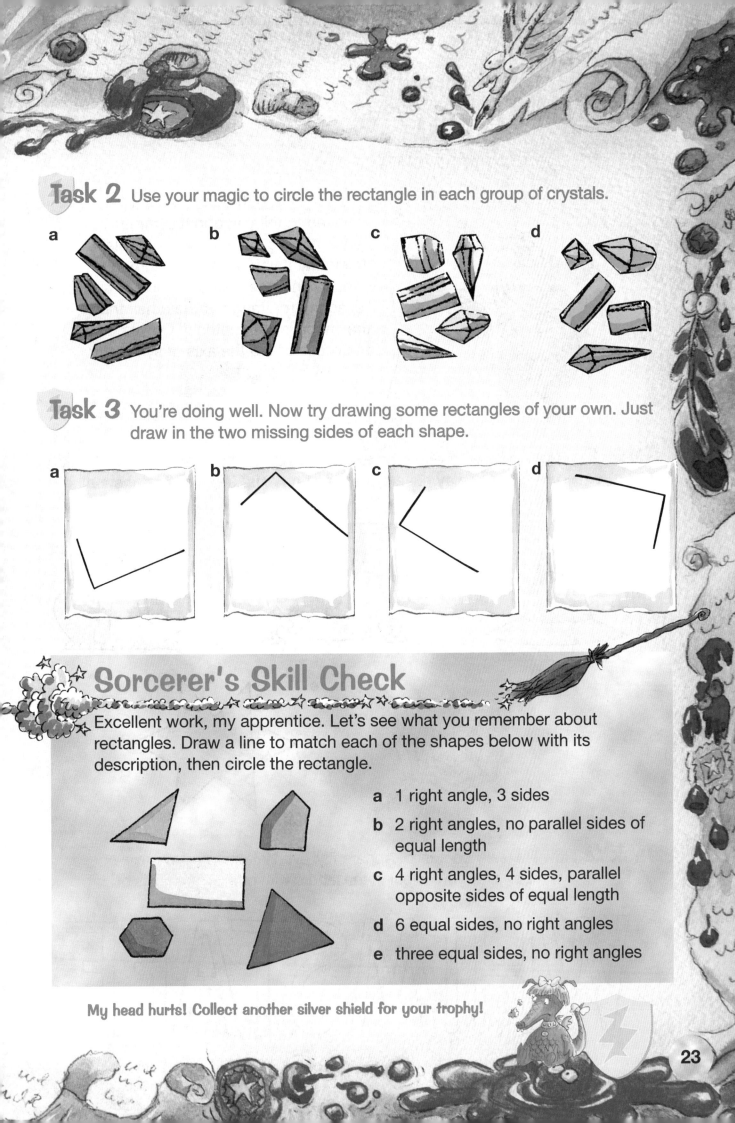

Task 3 You're doing well. Now try drawing some rectangles of your own. Just draw in the two missing sides of each shape.

a   b   c   d

Sorcerer's Skill Check

Excellent work, my apprentice. Let's see what you remember about rectangles. Draw a line to match each of the shapes below with its description, then circle the rectangle.

a 1 right angle, 3 sides

b 2 right angles, no parallel sides of equal length

c 4 right angles, 4 sides, parallel opposite sides of equal length

d 6 equal sides, no right angles

e three equal sides, no right angles

My head hurts! Collect another silver shield for your trophy!

Silly Symmetry

Oh dear!
I need to tell you about symmetry and I always get in such a muddle! I think that if you draw a line through a shape and one side of the line is an exact mirror image of the other, then the shape is symmetrical. Oh yes, and the line is called the axis of symmetry.

Task 1 Help! We have to draw the axes of symmetry in these shapes. I think some of them may have more than one axis. Can you find them all?

a

b

c

d

e

Task 2 Now I'm really confused! Apparently, even letters can have axis of symmetry. Can you colour in the letters with one or more axis of symmetry?

WHIMSTAFF

Task 3 Dabracababra! Now can you draw in the missing parts of these shapes?

a   b   c   d

Task 4 I like drawing two pictures on my magic parchment, then folding it down the middle. Can you draw a circle around the parchments where the pictures are symmetrical?

a

b

c

Sorcerer's Skill Check

My head hurts. Wizard Whimstaff's collection of symmetrical things has got muddled up with non-symmetrical shapes. Can you circle the symmetrical shapes?

Super! Collect another silver shield for your trophy!

Batty Bar Charts

To be a maths wizard you need to be able to read the bar charts in my spell books. Bar charts allow you to look at and compare different types of data using bars of different lengths. Don't worry if it seems hard at first.

Task 1 Here's a bar chart from my spell book. Have a good look, then answer the questions. Hey presto!

spiders   bats' wings   cobwebs   beetles   snails' tails   flies

a Which ingredient does the spell need the most of? _____

b How many beetles do I need for the spell? _____

c Which ingredient does the spell need the least of? _____

d Which two ingredients does the spell need three of? _____

and _____

Task 2 Well done! These bar charts have some of their bars missing. Can you look at the leftover ingredients in the jars, then draw in the missing bars?

a

b

26

Task 3 Abracadabra! Tables are another way of displaying data. This table tells you about some of the things you'll find in my cave. It contains all the information you need to work your magic and complete the bar chart.

Broomsticks	3
Cauldrons	2
Potion bottles	5
Crystal balls	4
Wizard hats	2

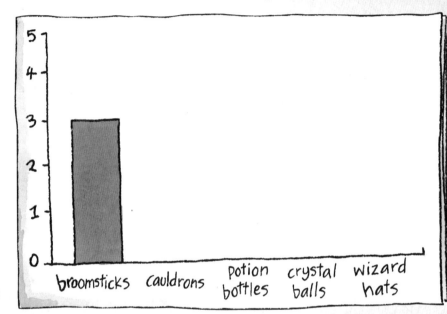

Sorcerer's Skill Check

Now let's see what you've learnt about bar charts and tables. The table and bar chart below show our scores from a game of Supernatural Snap. There are gaps in both but all the information is there to complete them.

Mugly & Bugly	2
Pointy	
Miss Snufflebeam	1
Wizard Whimstaff	

Croak! We're off for a snooze. Collect another shield for your trophy.

Apprentice Wizard Challenge 2

Challenge 1 Circle the biggest in each of these pairs.

a 20mm   2m   **b** 120cm   1m   **c** 180m   2km

d 2kg   250g   **e** 3 litres   3500ml

Challenge 2 Sort these shapes by colouring regular polygons blue and irregular polygons purple. Then draw and colour two polygons of your own; one regular and one irregular.

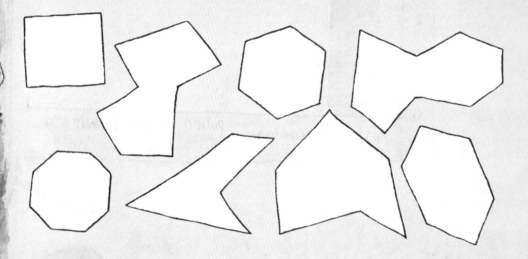

Challenge 3 Draw hands on these clock faces to match the digital readouts.

a   **b**   **c**

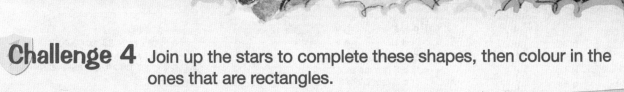

Challenge 4 Join up the stars to complete these shapes, then colour in the ones that are rectangles.

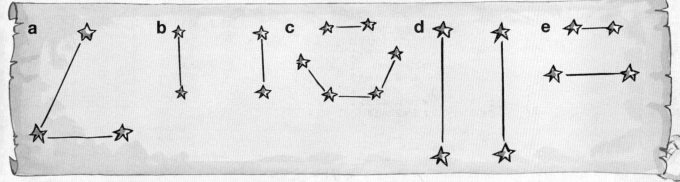

a   b   c   d   e

Challenge 5 Draw in the lines of symmetry.

a   b   c   d

Challenge 6 Look at the bar chart and answer these questions.

a   How many frogs does Wizard Whimstaff have?   _____

b   Which ingredient does he have most of?   _____

c   How many snails does he have?   _____

d   Which ingredient does he have least of?   _____

Count how many challenges you got right and put stars on the test tube
to show your score. Then take the last silver shield for your trophy!

6

5

4

3

2

1

Challenge Score

Answers

Pages 2–3
Task 1   **a** <   **b** >   **c** <
       d =   **e** <   **f** >

Task 2   **a** 11   **b** 15   **c** 6
       d 49   **e** 54   **f** 12

Task 3   **a** true   **b** false   **c** true
       d true   **e** false   **f** false

Sorcerer's Skill Check
     a >   **b** =   **c** >
     d =   **e** <   **f** <

Pages 4–5
Task 1   **a** 20   **d** 110   **g** 200
       b 50   **e** 100   **h** 400
       c 90   **f** 200

Task 2   **a** any number from 32–34
       b any number from 17–19
       c any number from 410–440
       d 7 or 8
       e any number from 88–92

Task 3   **a** 111   **b** 263   **c** 177
       d 88   **e** 312   **f** 228

Task 4   **a** $\frac{1}{2}$ **b** $\frac{2}{3}$ **c** $\frac{1}{4}$ **d** $\frac{3}{4}$

Sorcerer's Skill Check
     a 35   **b** 16   **c** 19
     d 120   **e** 26

Pages 6–7
Task 1   **a** each frog gets 3 flies
         with 1 remainder
       b each frog gets 3 flies
         with 1 remainder
       c each frog gets 2 flies
         with 2 remainder
       d each frog gets 1 fly
         with 3 remainder
       e each frog gets 1 fly
         with 1 remainder
       f each frog gets 1 fly
         with 2 remainder

Task 2   **a** 6 remainder 1   **f** 6 remainder 3
       b 3 remainder 1   **g** 9 remainder 1
       c 2 remainder 1   **h** 5 remainder 2
       d 1 remainder 3   **i** 11 remainder 2
       e 5 remainder 2   **j** 12 remainder 1

Task 3   **a** 125p or £1.25
       b 120p or £1.20
       c 150p or £1.50
       d 250cm or 2.50m
       e 225cm or 2.25m
       f 225cm or 2.25m

Task 4   **a** 10   **b** 13   **c** 21
       d 24   **e** 28

Sorcerer's Skill Check
     Bold answers should be coloured.
     a 5 remainder 2
        5 remainder 4
     b 1 remainder 2
        1 remainder 3
     c **4 remainder 3**
        4 remainder 2

Pages 8–9
Task 1   **a** 6, 8, 18   **d** 20, 35, 45
       b 6, 15, 24   **e** 40, 50, 90
       c 8, 12, 32

Task 2   **a** 4   **b** 7   **c** 12
       d 10   **e** 7

Task 3   **a** 4 groups of 4 flies
       b 6 groups of 2 flies
       c 3 groups of 3 flies
       d 3 groups of 5 flies
       e 2 groups of 10 flies

Sorcerer's Skill Check
     Matching pairs are:
     a 3×4 and 6×2
     b 2×3 and 3×2
     c 4×4 and 8×2
     d 2×10 and 5×4
     e 5×3 and 3×5
     f 2×2 and 4×1

Pages 10–11
Task 1   **a**

       b

       c

       d

Task 2   **a** $\frac{3}{4}$ **b** $\frac{1}{2}$
       c $\frac{1}{4}$ **d** $1\frac{1}{2}$

Task 3   **a** $\frac{3}{2}$ **d** $\frac{5}{4}$
       b $\frac{4}{3}$ **e** $\frac{8}{4}$
       c $\frac{5}{2}$ **f** $\frac{9}{4}$

Task 4   Matching pairs are:
     a $1\frac{1}{2}$ and $1\frac{1}{2}$ **d** $\frac{3}{4}$ and $2\frac{1}{4}$
     b $\frac{1}{2}$ and $2\frac{1}{2}$ **e** $2\frac{1}{5}$ and $\frac{4}{5}$
     c $\frac{1}{3}$ and $2\frac{2}{3}$

Sorcerer's Skill Check
     a 3   **b** 15
     c $3\frac{3}{4}$ **d** 1

Pages 12–13
Task 1   **a** 3.3, 3.6, 3.9
       b 2.24, 2.27, 2.31
       c 10.4, 10.5, 10.7, 10.8, 10.9
       d 6.92, 6.93, 6.96, 6.97, 7.00

Task 2   **a** 125p   **b** 699p   **c** 980p
       d £3.80   **e** £9.40   **f** £7.68

Task 3   The matching pairs are:
     1.25m and 125cm
     0.5m and 50cm
     130cm and 1.3m
     2.8m and 280cm

Task 4   **a** 0.5   **d** $\frac{3}{4}$
       b 0.25   **e** $\frac{9}{10}$
       c 0.1

Sorcerer's Skill Check
     a 99p, £1.99, 235p, £2.40
     b 1m, 135cm, 201cm, 895cm
     c $2\frac{1}{2}$ cm, 58cm, 99cm, 242cm

Pages 14–15
Challenge 1
     a >   **b** =   **c** <
     d >   **e** >   **f** =

Challenge 2
     a 100   **d** 50
     b 50   **e** 75
     c 100

Challenge 3
     The following lily pads should be
     coloured in: b, c, d, f, g, h, j

Challenge 4

x	2	3	4	5	10
2	4	6	8	10	20
3	6	9	12	15	30
4	8	12	16	20	40
5	10	15	20	25	50
10	20	30	40	50	100

Challenge 5

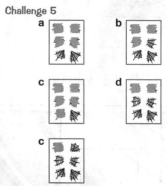

     The order is: **e, d, b, a, c**

Challenge 6
     a $\frac{1}{4}$ **d** $1\frac{1}{2}$
     b $\frac{3}{4}$ **e** $2\frac{3}{4}$
     c $\frac{1}{10}$

Pages 16–17
Task 1   **a** 3kg   **b** 1250ml
       c 550cm   **d** 110cm

Task 2   **a** 250ml   **b** 400ml
       c 2000ml or 2 litres

Task 3   **a** 2kg or 2000g
       b 600g
       c 1250g or 1.25kg

Task 4   **a** 132cm
       b 5m
       c 400cm

Sorcerer's Skill Check
     a 8cm = 80mm
     b 2 litres = 2000ml
     c 100cm = 1m
     d 4000g = 4kg
     e 2000m = 2km

Pages 18–19

Task 1

Task 2
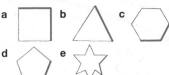

Task 3
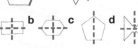

a, **b** and **d** should be coloured in.

Task 4
a This shape has 5 sides and 2 right angles. It has 1 line of symmetry.
b This shape has 4 sides and 4 right angles. It has 4 lines of symmetry.
c This shape has 3 sides and 0 right angles. It has 3 lines of symmetry.
d This shape has 6 sides and 2 right angles. It has 0 lines of symmetry.

Sorcerer's Skill Check
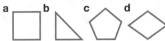

Pages 20–21

Task 1

Task 2   a 5:00   b 18:30
          c 20:45   d 2:20

Task 3 Your numbers should be in the order b, f, d, c, e, a

Sorcerer's Skill Check
a

b

c

d

Pages 22–23

Task 1 a Yes, No, Yes, No
       b No, No, No, No
       c Yes, Yes, Yes, Yes
       d No, No, No, No

Task 2 a

b

c

d

Task 3
a

b

c
d

Sorcerer's Skill Check
blue shape – a
orange shape – b
yellow shape – c
purple shape – d
red shape – e
Shape c is the rectangle.

Pages 24–25

Task 1
a

b

c

d

c

Task 2

Task 3
a

b

c

d

Task 4
a

b

c

Sorcerer's Skill Check
Symmetrical shapes:

Non-symmetrical shapes:

Pages 26–27

Task 1 a spiders   b 4
       c cobwebs   d flies and snails' tails

Task 2 a spider bar should reach 2 on vertical axis
       b rainbow bar should reach 3 and magic crystal bar 1 on vertical axis

Task 3 Bars should reach:
       Broomsticks   3
       Cauldrons   2
       Potion bottles   5
       Crystal balls   4
       Wizard hats   2

Sorcerer's Skill Check
       Bars should reach:
       Mugly & Bugly   2
       Pointy   3
       Miss Snufflebeam 1
       Wizard Whimstaff 5

Pages 28–29

Challenge 1
       a 2m   d 2kg
       b 120cm   e 3500ml
       c 2km

Challenge 2

Challenge 3
a

b

c

Challenge 4
a

d

b

e

c

Challenge 5
a

b

c
d

Challenge 6
       a 7   b flies
       c 3   d spiders

Wizard's Trophy of Excellence

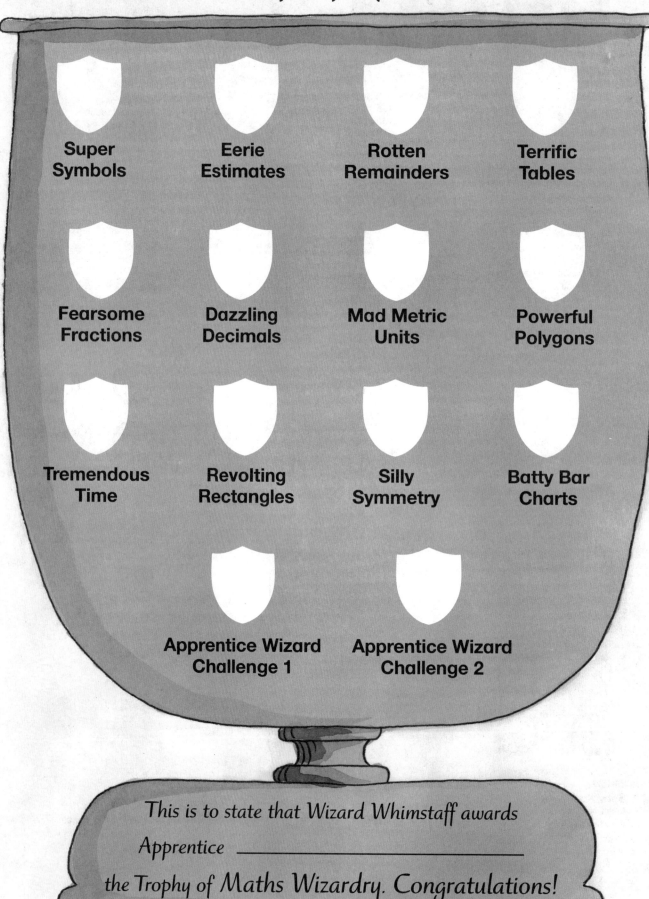

Super Symbols

Eerie Estimates

Rotten Remainders

Terrific Tables

Fearsome Fractions

Dazzling Decimals

Mad Metric Units

Powerful Polygons

Tremendous Time

Revolting Rectangles

Silly Symmetry

Batty Bar Charts

Apprentice Wizard Challenge 1

Apprentice Wizard Challenge 2

This is to state that Wizard Whimstaff awards

Apprentice _____

the Trophy of Maths Wizardry. Congratulations!